# I ♥ PUPS

## This book belongs to

. . . . . . . . . . . . . . . . . . . . . . . . . . . . . . . . . . . . . . . . . .

. . . . . . . . . . . . . . . . . . . . . . . . . . . . . . . . . . . . . . . . .

Written by Heather Dakota

Designed by Sandra Bruner and Ali Castro

Cover design by Flora Chan

Tangerine Press

an imprint of

**SCHOLASTIC**

www.scholastic.com

Copyright © 2016 Scholastic Inc.
Scholastic, Tangerine Press, and associated logos are trademarks and/or registered trademarks of Scholastic Inc.
Published by Tangerine Press, an imprint of Scholastic Inc., 557 Broadway, New York, NY 10012

Scholastic Canada Ltd., Markham, Ontario
Scholastic Australia Pty. Ltd., Gosford, NSW
Scholastic New Zealand Ltd., Greenmount, Auckland

10 9 8 7 6 5 4 3 2
ISBN: 978-1-338-03382-3

Printed and bound in Jiaxing, China

W9-BUU-182

1

## Who can resist them?

Not you, that's for sure—and that's why you're reading this book! Get ready for a celebration of all things canine. From pooch-tastic games to dog-related quizzes and bark-a-licious puppy puzzles, it's all here! Grab your favorite pup, get comfy, and curl up for a seriously fun doggy extravaganza!

# Quiz!

# Which furry friend is right for you?

There are hundreds of dog breeds. How can you choose the one that's right for you? Take this quiz, and find out which pooch is a perfect match for you.

**1. What kind of human friends do you like to hang out with?**

- **a** Just my best friend. We do everything together.
- **b** Everyone! If you've got it, flaunt it.
- **c** Mainly people who play on my team
- **d** A small group of friends and family

**2. What award would you be most likely to win?**

- **a** Most thoughtful
- **b** Best hair
- **c** Bravest
- **d** Best practical jokes

### 3. What best describes your favorite outfit?

**a** Something easy and comfortable

**b** Definitely something that looks amazing, even if it's uncomfortable

**c** Clothes with patterns—lots of patterns

**d** Probably a T-shirt with a funny saying

### 4. What would you like to do on a Saturday?

**a** Play around in the backyard

**b** Get my hair done

**c** Go on an adventure

**d** Play hide-and-seek with some friends

### 5. You want a dog that likes to be:

**a** Part of the action

**b** The princess

**c** Out and about

**d** In your lap

Mostly s

## LOYAL LABRADOR

Labradors—or Labs, for short—are known for being very loyal. They love their people and people love them. The most common colors for Labs are yellow, chocolate, and black.

Mostly s

## PRECIOUS POODLE

Poodles walk around with their heads held high. They are the supermodels of the canine world and come in a variety of colors including white, brown, and black. They have grace and style and love to be pampered.

Mostly ⓒs

## DASHING DALMATIAN

Dalmatians are white dogs with black spots. They are brave and excitable and love to explore new things. They are famous for being service dogs and riding around on fire trucks.

Mostly ⓓs

## PLAYFUL PUG

Pugs are a small breed of dog, about the size of a large cat. They are energetic, playful, and love to sit in your lap. Getting attention from you is their favorite thing to do.

# What Does the Puppy Say?

# My Adorable Dog

**Check off all of the things that are doggone great for you.**

[ ] Great sniffer

[ ] Small and cuddly

[ ] Really active

[ ] Good working dog

[ ] Just your average pup

[ ] Quiet

[ ] Tries to talk

[ ] Deep bark

[ ] Long tail

[ ] Short tail

[ ] Happy

[ ] Likes to chill on the couch

[ ] Likes to be outside

[ ] Likes to sit in my lap

[ ] Adopted

[ ] Free

[ ] Purebred

[ ] Mixed breed

[ ] Always with me

[ ] Likes his alone time

[ ] Sleeps with me

[ ] Sleeps on the floor

[ ] Blue eyes

[ ] Brown eyes

[ ] **Different-colored eyes**

[ ] Super funny

[ ] **Adorable**

[ ] Good watchdog

[ ] **Really smart**

[ ] Acts like a cat

[ ] **Needs a lot of exercise**

[ ] Needs just a little exercise

[ ] **Likes to play games**

[ ] Lives inside

[ ] Lives outside

[ ] **Needs a lot of grooming**

[ ] Does not need grooming

[ ] **Likes the water**

[ ] Tiny

[ ] **Small**

[ ] Medium

[ ] **Large**

[ ] Well trained

[ ] **Best buds**

# Puppy Playdate

Help your puppy find his friend
so they can play ball.

START
HERE →

Answer on Page 94.

# Pup-arazzi

What is your pup's fashion style? Take the quiz and find out.

## 1. What do you like to do on the weekends?

**a** Stay home to read a book
**b** Go to the mall with friends
**c** Go to the park
**d** Go on a bike ride

## 2. How many close friends do you have?

**a** 1 or 2
**b** At least 10
**c** 3 or 4
**d** Enough for a team

## 3. How much do you like things to change?

**a** It's OK, if I'm in charge.
**b** Only as much my friends do
**c** All the time
**d** Don't like change

## 4. How long does it take you to decide what to wear?

**a** I'm super-quick
**b** Sometimes an hour or more
**c** Everyday casual = fast; going out = 30 minutes
**d** T-shirts and jeans, right?

## 5. What is your favorite part of the fashion world?

**a** Clothing designers
**b** Models
**c** Makeup artists
**d** Eh, not my thing

**6. What is your favorite outdoor activity?**

a Painting

b Whatever my friends are doing

c Biking solo or with my friends

d Playing some kind of sport

**9. What is the style you love most?**

a Mysterious and unique

b Spicy and hot

c Fresh and sweet

d Sporty and fun

**7. How do you like to study?**

a By myself

b With all of my friends

c Outside

d At the library

**10. If your life was a movie, it would be...**

a A romance

b A drama

c A comedy

d An action-adventure

**8. How do you like to wear your hair?**

a In a funky do

b So many ways, so little time

c Natural

d A ponytail works great!

Mostly **a**s

## YOU'RE A SUPERSTAR!

Those are stars in your dog's eyes, and he or she should look the part. Sunglasses and cute cuts will be perfect!

Mostly **b**s

## WHAT A POSH PUPPY!

Your pup is a glam girl or it boy and wants to be the center of attention, just like you. With your dramatic flair and flashy style, be sure to accessorize with a fancy leash and carrying bag.

Mostly **c**s

## AU NATURALE IS YOUR POOCH'S STYLE!

Go with your instincts. A good bath and a quick comb may be all that your dog needs. A cute bandanna wouldn't hurt either!

Mostly **d**s

## IT'S ALL ABOUT ADVENTURE!

Your dog wants to be active, so there is very little time for being fashion forward. Make sure you have a dog water bottle, and you're all set!

# Puppy Finder

w! What a mess! Has your room ever been so messy
t you couldn't find your puppy BFF? Then you
w what to do. Search this page high and low and
f you can find a hidden puppy or two.

Answer on Page 94.

19

# Super-Pup Picker

Choose either-or, then follow the flow chart and see what a cool pup you would be.

**Would you rather be outside or inside during a sunny day?**

Outside

**Do you like to dance or tell jokes?**

Meat

Movie star

Inside

No

**Do you prefer a meat or just cheese on your pizza?**

Start Here!

**Do you remember to do your homework?**

**Would you rather be a movie star or a sports star?**

Cheese

Yes

English

Math

Hamburgers

**Which subject do you like best, English or Math?**

**Do you like hot dogs or hamburgers?**

Hot dogs

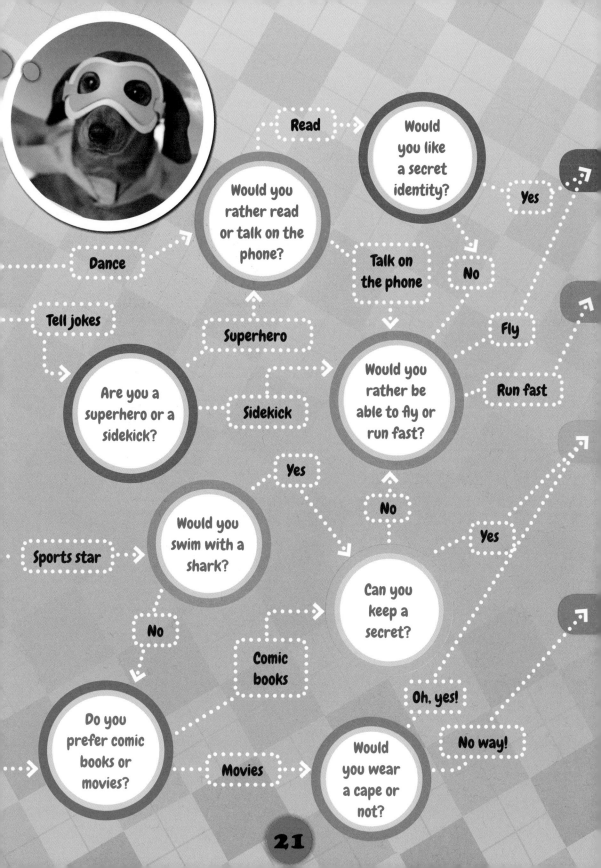

Read

Would you like a secret identity?

Would you rather read or talk on the phone?

Dance

Yes

Talk on the phone

No

Tell jokes

Superhero

Fly

Are you a superhero or a sidekick?

Sidekick

Would you rather be able to fly or run fast?

Run fast

Yes

No

Sports star

Would you swim with a shark?

Yes

Can you keep a secret?

No

Comic books

Oh, yes!

Do you prefer comic books or movies?

Movies

Would you wear a cape or not?

No way!

## SUPER-POOCH

You are one fly pup! You have a secret identity that no one but your closest friends know. Flying is your superpower!

## WONDER DOG

You are a wonder! Everyone looks up to you and your wonderful ways. Running at super-speeds is your superpower!

## BAT BOWWOW

Who was that masked dog? Your secret identity is safe behind your mask. Your superpower is your intelligence. You are one smart cookie!

## ROBO-PUP

You are one powerful puppy! Your superpower is to combine your smarts with know-how to create a suit that makes you invincible.

23

# Colorful Pooch

Color in the puppy design. Use colored pencils or crayons so the colors won't leak onto the other pages.

# Snow Puppy

There is nothing cuter than a puppy all snuggled up in a sweater. What color will you make his winter clothes?

# Surf Dog

Color in this righteous pup!

# Puppy By-the-Numbers

Use the numbers as your guide to color in the doggies.

Answer on Page 94.

# Doggy Doodles

Use the prompts to finish the drawings on these pages.

Draw your favorite dog into this scene.

If your dog could buy pup-cakes, what would they look like?

# The Dog Wash

A clean best friend is a happy best friend!
Add more puppies to this dog wash. Then color it in!

# Truth About Dogs!

List all of the facts that you know about dogs.

1

2

3

4

5

6

7

8

9

10

# Things You May Not Know About Dogs!

**Check off the facts you already knew.**

**1** [ ] It's a myth that dogs are color-blind. They can see color, but not as vividly as you can.

**2** [ ] Dogs' only sweat glands are between their paw pads. They pant instead of sweat to regulate their temperature.

**3** [ ] A dog's mouth applies 150–200 pounds of pressure per square inch.

**4** [ ] A one-year-old dog is as physically mature as a 15-year-old human.

**5** [ ] Dogs can be trained to detect diseases, seizures, and other health issues in humans.

**6** [ ] Dogs have no sense of time.

**7** [ ] Humans have kept dogs as pets for more than 12,000 years.

**8** [ ] A dog's sense of smell is more than 100,000 times stronger than a human's.

**9** [ ] All dogs are direct descendants of wolves.

**10** [ ] A dog's nose print is as unique as human's fingerprint.

# Insta-Pup

Your puppy can't take a selfie,
but you can take them for him.
Add your pup's selfies on this page.

PLACE IMAGE HERE PLACE IMAGE HERE PLACE IMAGE HERE PLACE IMAGE HEREPLACE IMAGE HERE PLACE IMAGE HERE PLACE IMAGE ♥ HERE ♥ PLACE IMAGE HERE PLACE IMAGE HERE ♥ PLACE IMAGE HERE

PLACE IMAGE HERE ♥ PLACE IMAGE HERE PLACE IMAGE HERE PLACE IMAGE HERE PLACE IMAGE HERE ♥ PLACE IMAGE HERE PLACE IMAGE ♥ HERE ♥ PLACE IMAGE HERE PLACE IMAGE HERE ♥ PLACE IMAGE HERE

PLACE IMAGE HERE ♥ PLACE IMAGE HERE PLACE IMAGE HERE PLACE IMAGE HERE PLACE IMAGE HERE ♥ PLACE IMAGE HERE PLACE IMAGE ♥ HERE ♥ PLACE IMAGE HERE PLACE IMAGE HERE ♥ PLACE IMAGE HERE

PLACE IMAGE HERE ♥ PLACE IMAGE HERE PLACE IMAGE HERE PLACE IMAGE HERE PLACE IMAGE HEREPLACE IMAGE HERE ♥ PLACE IMAGE ♥ HERE ♥ PLACE IMAGE HERE PLACE IMAGE HERE ♥ PLACE IMAGE HERE

PLACE IMAGE HERE ♥ PLACE IMAGE HERE PLACE IMAGE HERE PLACE IMAGE HEREPLACE IMAGE HERE ♥ PLACE IMAGE HERE PLACE IMAGE ♥ HERE ♥ PLACE IMAGE HERE PLACE IMAGE HERE ♥ PLACE IMAGE HERE

#ilovepups

PLACE IMAGE HERE ♥
PLACE IMAGE HERE PLACE
IMAGE HERE PLACE IMAGE
HEREPLACE IMAGE HERE ♥
PLACE IMAGE HERE PLACE
IMAGE ♥ HERE ♥ PLACE
IMAGE HERE PLACE IMAGE
HERE ♥ PLACE IMAGE HERE

PLACE IMAGE HERE ♥
PLACE IMAGE HERE PLACE
IMAGE HERE PLACE IMAGE
HERE PLACE IMAGE HERE ♥
PLACE IMAGE HERE PLACE
IMAGE ♥ HERE ♥ PLACE
IMAGE HERE PLACE IMAGE
HERE ♥ PLACE IMAGE HERE

PLACE IMAGE HERE ♥
PLACE IMAGE HERE PLACE
IMAGE HERE PLACE IMAGE
HERE PLACE IMAGE HERE ♥
PLACE IMAGE HERE PLACE
IMAGE ♥ HERE ♥ PLACE
IMAGE HERE PLACE IMAGE
HERE ♥ PLACE IMAGE HERE

PLACE IMAGE HERE ♥
PLACE IMAGE HERE PLACE
IMAGE HERE PLACE IMAGE
HERE PLACE IMAGE HERE ♥
PLACE IMAGE HERE PLACE
IMAGE ♥ HERE ♥ PLACE
IMAGE HERE PLACE IMAGE
HERE ♥ PLACE IMAGE HERE

PLACE IMAGE HERE
PLACE IMAGE HERE PLACE
IMAGE HERE PLACE IMAGE
HERE PLACE IMAGE HERE ♥
PLACE IMAGE HERE PLACE
IMAGE ♥ HERE ♥ PLACE
IMAGE HERE PLACE IMAGE
HERE ♥ PLACE IMAGE HERE

PLACE IMAGE HERE ♥
PLACE IMAGE HERE PLACE
IMAGE HERE PLACE IMAGE
HEREPLACE IMAGE HERE ♥
PLACE IMAGE HERE PLACE
IMAGE ♥ HERE ♥ PLACE
IMAGE HERE PLACE IMAGE
HERE ♥ PLACE IMAGE HERE

PLACE IMAGE HERE ♥
PLACE IMAGE HERE PLACE
IMAGE HERE PLACE IMAGE
HERE PLACE IMAGE HERE ♥
PLACE IMAGE HERE PLACE
IMAGE ♥ HERE ♥ PLACE
IMAGE HERE PLACE IMAGE
HERE ♥ PLACE IMAGE HERE

PLACE IMAGE HERE PLACE IMAGE HERE PLACE IMAGE HERE PLACE IMAGE HEREPLACE IMAGE HERE ♥ PLACE IMAGE HERE PLACE IMAGE ♥ HERE ♥ PLACE IMAGE HERE PLACE IMAGE HERE ♥ PLACE IMAGE HERE

PLACE IMAGE HERE PLACE IMAGE HERE PLACE IMAGE HERE PLACE IMAGE HEREPLACE IMAGE HERE ♥ PLACE IMAGE HERE PLACE IMAGE ♥ HERE ♥ PLACE IMAGE HERE PLACE IMAGE HERE ♥ PLACE IMAGE HERE

PLACE IMAGE HERE PLACE IMAGE HERE PLACE IMAGE HERE PLACE IMAGE HEREPLACE IMAGE HERE ♥ PLACE IMAGE HERE PLACE IMAGE ♥ HERE ♥ PLACE IMAGE HERE PLACE IMAGE HERE ♥ PLACE IMAGE HERE

PLACE IMAGE HERE PLACE IMAGE HERE PLACE IMAGE HERE PLACE IMAGE HERE PLACE IMAGE HERE PLACE IMAGE ♥ HERE ♥ PLACE IMAGE HERE PLACE IMAGE

PLACE IMAGE HERE ♥ PLACE IMAGE HERE PLACE IMAGE HERE PLACE IMAGE HERE PLACE IMAGE HERE ♥ PLACE IMAGE HERE PLACE IMAGE ♥ HERE ♥ PLACE IMAGE HERE PLACE IMAGE HERE ♥ PLACE IMAGE HERE

PLACE IMAGE HERE PLACE IMAGE HERE PLACE IMAGE HERE PLACE IMAGE HEREPLACE IMAGE HERE ♥ PLACE IMAGE HERE PLACE IMAGE ♥ HERE ♥ PLACE IMAGE HERE PLACE IMAGE HERE ♥ PLACE IMAGE HERE

PLACE IMAGE HERE ♥ PLACE IMAGE HERE PLACE IMAGE HERE PLACE IMAGE HERE PLACE IMAGE HERE ♥ PLACE IMAGE HERE PLACE IMAGE ♥ HERE ♥ PLACE IMAGE HERE PLACE IMAGE HERE ♥ PLACE IMAGE HERE

PLACE IMAGE HERE
PLACE IMAGE HERE PLACE
IMAGE HERE PLACE IMAGE
HERE PLACE IMAGE HERE ♥
PLACE IMAGE HERE PLACE
IMAGE ♥ HERE ♥ PLACE
IMAGE HERE PLACE IMAGE
HERE ♥ PLACE IMAGE HERE

PLACE IMAGE HERE ♥
PLACE IMAGE HERE PLACE
IMAGE HERE PLACE IMAGE
HERE PLACE IMAGE HERE ♥
PLACE IMAGE HERE PLACE
IMAGE ♥ HERE ♥ PLACE
IMAGE HERE PLACE IMAGE
HERE ♥ PLACE IMAGE HERE

PLACE IMAGE HERE
PLACE IMAGE HERE PLACE
IMAGE HERE PLACE IMAGE
HEREPLACE IMAGE HERE ♥
PLACE IMAGE HERE PLACE
IMAGE ♥ HERE ♥ PLACE
IMAGE HERE PLACE IMAGE
HERE ♥ PLACE IMAGE HERE

PLACE IMAGE HERE
PLACE IMAGE HERE PLACE
IMAGE HERE PLACE IMAGE
HERE PLACE IMAGE HERE ♥
PLACE IMAGE HERE PLACE
IMAGE ♥ HERE ♥ PLACE
IMAGE HERE PLACE IMAGE
HERE ♥ PLACE IMAGE HERE

PLACE IMAGE HERE ♥
PLACE IMAGE HERE PLACE
IMAGE HERE PLACE IMAGE
HEREPLACE IMAGE HERE ♥
PLACE IMAGE HERE PLACE
IMAGE ♥ HERE ♥ PLACE
IMAGE HERE PLACE IMAGE
HERE ♥ PLACE IMAGE HERE

PLACE IMAGE HERE ♥
PLACE IMAGE HERE PLACE
IMAGE HERE PLACE IMAGE
HEREPLACE IMAGE HERE ♥
PLACE IMAGE HERE PLACE
IMAGE ♥ HERE ♥ PLACE
IMAGE HERE PLACE IMAGE
HERE ♥ PLACE IMAGE HERE

#puppylove

# All About My Puppy

Write all about your puppy or the one you really want.

# Bow WOW Awards

Check off which awards you would give to your dog.

BEST PERSONALITY

BEST SMILE

FRIENDLIEST

MOST LOYAL

BEST TRICKS

BEST LISTENER

BEST EYES

MOST PAWPULAR

BEST JUMPER

SMARTEST

MOST OUTGOING

MOST OBEDIENT

MOST ATHLETIC

BEST SNIFFER

BIGGEST HERO

BEST FUR

SHYEST

BEST NAME

FUNNIEST

MOST LIKE A CAT

BEST DRESSED

43

# Wild Canine Quiz!

Which wild dog are you most like? Take the quiz and find out.

**1. You make plans with a friend and she cancels. What do you do?**

a Call up another friend and hang out

b Feel hurt because you were looking forward to it

c Have fun at home

d Think, "Whatever. Things happen."

**2. What do you most like to eat?**

a Steak

b Chicken

c Something unusual

d Lamb chops

**3. What adjective would you use to describe yourself?**

a Strong

b Quick

c Adaptable

d Smart

**4. What do you like to do at night?**

a Look at the moon and the stars

b Raid the fridge

c Sleep

d Everything—I love being up at night.

**5. Which would you rather be?**

- a  Cold
- b  Wet
- c  Hot
- d  Muddy

**6. What do you like to do on a nice day?**

- a  Hang out with friends
- b  Walk around in the woods
- c  Have fun close to home
- d  Sleep

**7. What is your favorite movie?**

- a  E.T.
- b  Frozen
- c  Despicable Me
- d  Home Alone

**8. How are you at parties?**

- a  I love my friends, but I'm shy around people I don't know.
- b  I'm pretty shy.
- c  Just show me the food table.
- d  I love being the clown.

**9. If you had a superpower, what would it be?**

- a  Mind reading
- b  Invisibility
- c  Night vision
- d  Sonic voice

**10. What is your favorite kind of dog?**

- a  Big dogs
- b  I like dogs, but I like cats too.
- c  A wild-looking dog
- d  A really active dog

Mostly **a**s

## YOU ARE A WOLF, FOR SURE.

You go with your gut instincts most of the time and you like your freedom. You are extremely intelligent and deal with your emotions well. And there is nothing more important than close friends and family.

Mostly **b**s

## A FOX IS THE WILD CANINE YOU'D BE.

You're a bit shy but strong and brave too. You are smart and energetic but also kind and loving. Taking time in the peace and silence of nature is perfect for you.

Mostly **c**s

## YOU'RE MOST LIKE A JACKAL.

Your careful, playful personality is a joy to your family and friends. There is nothing you like better than hanging out in the neighborhood or your house with family and friends.

Mostly **d**s

## YOU ARE A TRICKY COYOTE.

You kind of like being alone, but your prankster nature can get you into a bit of trouble. However, people love your sense of humor, and there is nothing that can stop you from getting what you want.

# Been There, Done That!

**Check off ALL of the things you've done with your dog.**

[ ] **Hosted a party**

[✓] Gone to a party

[ ] **Gone to a patio restaurant**

[ ] Volunteered

[ ] **Gone to the vet**

[ ] Visited the library

[ ] **Taken a trip to a dog park**

[✓] Gone swimming

[✓] **Played tag**

[ ] Danced in the rain

[✓] Given him or her a bath with the hose

[✓] **Gone for an extra-long walk**

[✓] Gone for a walk and let your dog lead the way

[✓] **Played in the snow**

[ ] Learned five new tricks

[ ] **Attended obedience school**

[✓] Dressed up

[✓] **Played Frisbee**

[ ] Visited a nursing home

[ ] Gone hiking

[ ] Played fetch until your dog was tired

[ ] Played hide-and-seek with a dog toy

[ ] Gone on vacation

[ ] Had a puppy playdate

[ ] Gone camping

[ ] Practiced doga (yoga with your dog)

[ ] Run an obstacle course

[✓] Taken a nap

[✓] Gone doggie shopping

[✓] Made a dog video

[ ] Organized a charity

[ ] Cooked for your dog

[ ] Gone for a car ride

[ ] Read a book together

[ ] Played in the sprinklers

[ ] Hosted a pet Olympics

[ ] Taken selfies

# Emoji-Pup

What mood are you in today? Write the date by the emoji-pup that shows how you feel.

# Every Dog Has His Day

**What does your dog do all day while you're gone?**

7:00 a.m.

8:00 a.m.

9:00 a.m.

10:00 a.m.

11:00 a.m.

noon

Make up a story if your dog is a napper.

1:00 p.m.

2:00 p.m.

3:00 p.m.

4:00 p.m.

5:00 p.m.

6:00 p.m.

# Canine Crossword

## Have fun filling out this crossword for puppy lovers.

### ACROSS

1 Another word for a dog's fur

3 The name of a dog breed that rhymes with holly

5 A dog kisses with this

6 A baby dog

8 A doctor for your dog

9 The way dogs communicate

10 You use this to walk your dog

### DOWN

1 The dog a lot of celebrities own

2 Your dog will itch and scratch if he catches these

3 A dog's longest tooth

4 What dogs bury

7 A group of dogs

9 Some dogs like to fetch this

Train your brain!

Answer on Page 94.

# This or That?

Circle the trait you like best about your dog.

ACTIVE or SLEEPY

ALERT or FLIGHTY

BEAUTIFUL or SCRUFFY

CAT FRIENDLY or DOG FRIENDLY

OBEDIENT or BULLHEADED

AFFECTIONATE or STANDOFFISH

CLEVER or SMART

CRATE-TRAINED
or
HOUSEBROKEN

BIG
or
LITTLE

ON A LEASH
or
RUNNING FREE

DEMANDING
or
INDEPENDENT

CUDDLY or CUTE

EAGER TO TRAIN
or
EAGER TO PLEASE

FAST
or
FLUFFY

ENERGETIC or SENSITIVE

HARDWORKING or SPORTY

OUTGOING or SHY

MELLOW or NERVOUS

LONG-HAIRED or SHORT-HAIRED

GRACEFUL or SWEET

MOODY or MISCHIEVOUS

GROOMING or NO GROOMING

BARKING
or
TAIL WAGGING

PUREBRED
or
MIXED

SILLY or ROWDY

STRONG or BRAVE

SPOTTED
or
COLORFUL

BOUNCING
or
FETCHING

GOOD NOSE
or
GOOD EYESIGHT

ON YOUR LAP
or
AT YOUR FEET

# Dot-to-Dot Doggie

Use your pencil to follow the numbers to create scenes for your puppy.

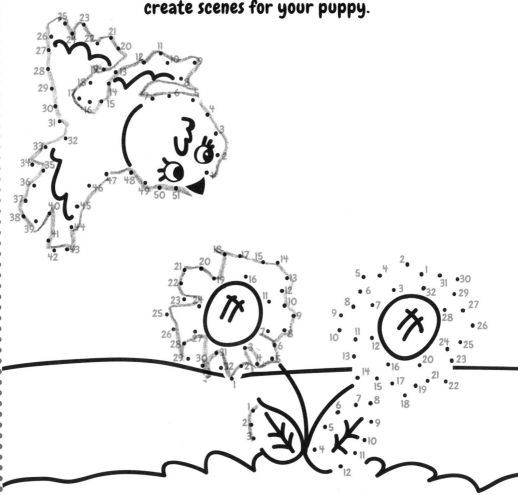

Answer on Page 95.

Answer on Page 95.

# Go Fetch!

Help your puppy find the stick.

START HERE →

Answer on Page 95.

# Pixel Pups

Use colored pencils or crayons to solve the puzzle and find the puppy in the pixel art.

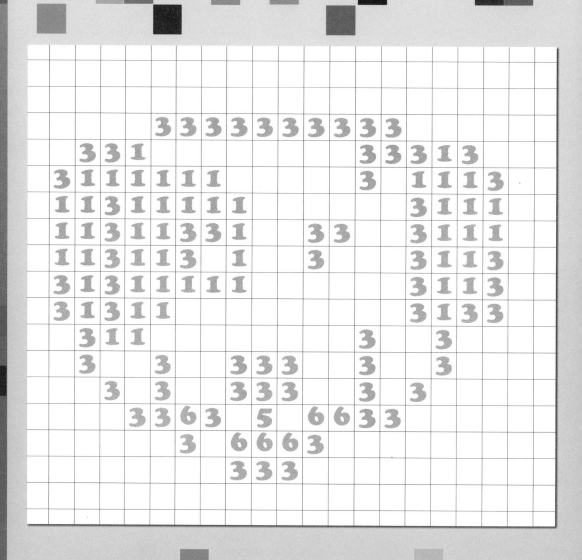

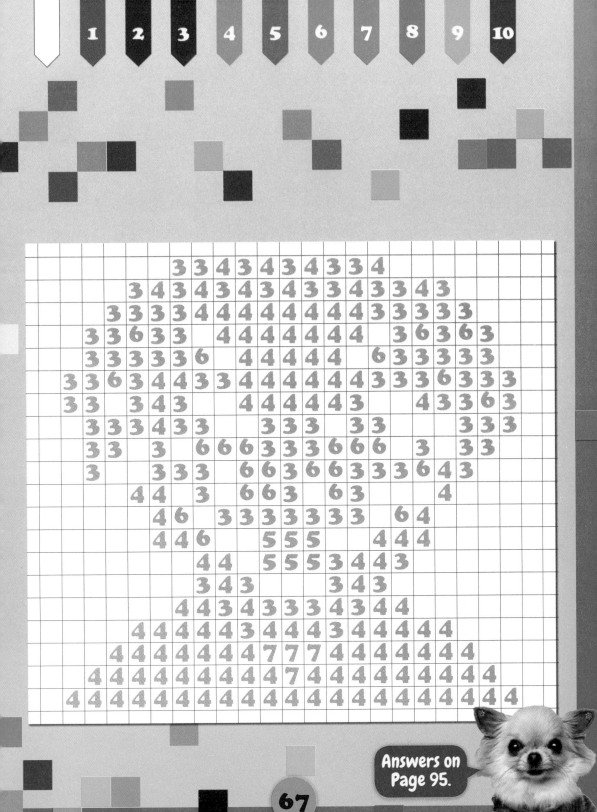

Answers on Page 95.

Answers on Page 95.

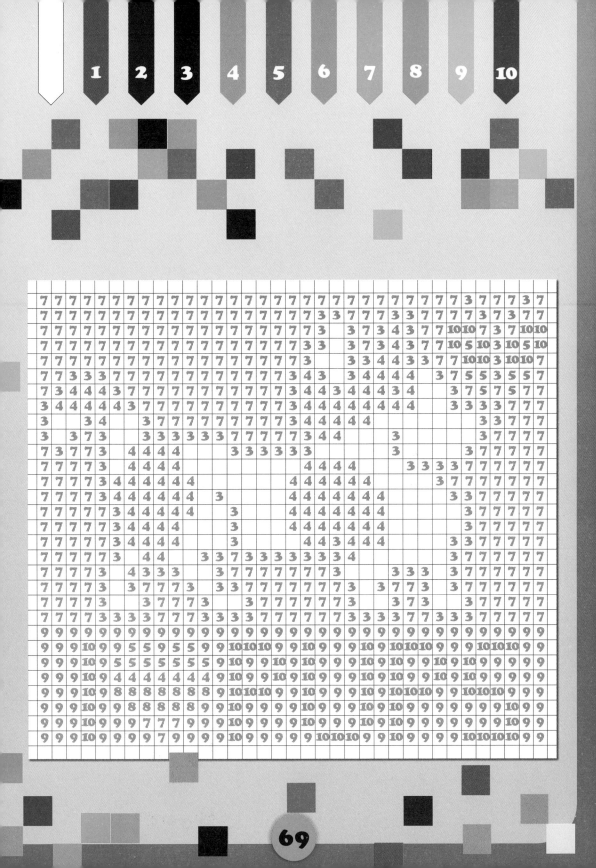

# Spy Pup

Help Spy Pup solve the secret message. Use the code to solve the puzzles.

 A  B  C  D

 E  F  G  H  I

 J  K  L  M  N

 O  P  Q 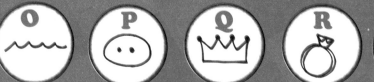 R  S

 T  U  V  W

 X  Y  Z

Answer on Page 95.

70

# Puppy Word Scramble

Oh no! These puppy words have gotten all mixed up. Won't you help a dog out and unscramble them?

1 INTARGIN _____

2 NBOE _____

3 DHTWOCAG _____

4 RKITCS _____

5 MLATEIYP _____

6 RKAB _____

7 ERTAC _____

8 ALHSE _____

9   YFRUR _____

10  HNIEW _____

11  RTEERRI _____

12  FLLAYPU _____

13  RTIETL _____

14  ABARDRLO _____

15  ILELCO _____

16  GABELE _____

17  XOREB _____

18  KHUYS _____

Answers on Page 96.

# Doggie Dreams

Write a story about your pup's latest dream. Write it from your puppy's viewpoint, and don't forget to use your sensory words.

_____

_____

_____

_____

_____

_____

_____

_____

_____

_____

_____

_____

_____

_____

_____

_____

_____

_____

_____

_____

# Your Dog Name

*If you were a dog, what would your name be?*

**You're about to find out!** Look at the charts on these pages. Use your birth date to find your puppy first name and your birth month to find your puppy last name. Let all of your friends try it too! Who has the best dog name?

## Birth date = First Name

| | | | | | |
|---|---|---|---|---|---|
| 1 | Molly | 11 | Amber | 21 | Peanut |
| 2 | Snoopy | 12 | Sassy | 22 | Shadow |
| 3 | Cookie | 13 | Bella | 23 | Coco |
| 4 | Lady | 14 | Toby | 24 | Lucky |
| 5 | Sparky | 15 | Princess | 25 | Missy |
| 6 | Mocha | 16 | Scooter | 26 | Buster |
| 7 | Trixie | 17 | Spike | 27 | Bailey |
| 8 | Pepper | 18 | Chloe | 28 | Taz |
| 9 | Muffin | 19 | Harley | 29 | Buddy |
| 10 | Bosco | 20 | Sheba | 30 | Lola |
| | | | | 31 | Boomer |

| Birth month | = | Last Name |
|---|---|---|
| January | | Barkley |
| February | | O'Leash |
| March | | Boneapart |
| April | | Furrier |
| May | | Growler |
| June | | Puppini |
| July | | Wolfson |
| August | | Fluffington |
| September | | Chowhound |
| October | | McBarksalot |
| November | | Lickster |
| December | | Fetcher |

**HELLO**
my name is

# Find the Dog

```
N N A M R E B O D D T U K J G
M A S T I F F S C N S Z M Q O
N T I E P R A H S A W T O C D
Z O H T T E O P M L D H H B L
R G L R A W I O I D J I S O L
E O I L C M Y L B N H H C X U
W T T H I E L E L U N S H E B
E R O T D P A A A O V D N R D
I W E D W G A H D F C E A N T
M D P T L E U P A W S E U W E
A N O E R A I T I E T O Z S R
R U I P A I I L G N H J E V R
A O N P O K E N E D U T R I I
N H T I A Q I V O R L R P K E
E Y E H H K Y O E A L U Q U R
R E R W E O L B M R G L W L O
G R R P E B D N U H S H C A D
S G S P O M E R A N I A N S Q
```

AKITA

BEAGLE

BLOODHOUND

BOXER

BULLDOG

CHIHUAHUA

CHOW CHOW

COLLIE

DACHSHUND

DALMATIAN

DOBERMAN

GREYHOUND

MALTESE

MASTIFF

NEWFOUNDLAND

PAPILLON

PEKINGESE

POINTER

POMERANIAN

PUG

RETRIEVER

ROTTWEILER

SALUKI

SAMOYED

SCHNAUZER

SHAR-PEI

SHIH TZU

TERRIER

WEIMARANER

WHIPPET

Answer on Page 96.

# Lost Puppy

Help the pup get back to her doghouse.

START
HERE →

Answer on Page 96.

# Very Funny

Here are a few jokes to get you and your puppy pals barking with laughter.

**Why are dalmatians terrible at hide-and-seek?**

They're always spotted!

**Why did the dog carry a clock?**

She wanted to be a watchdog!

**What happens when it rains cats and dogs?**

You can step in a poodle.

**What kind of dog does Dracula have?**

A bloodhound

What happened when the dog went to the flea circus?

He stole the show!

Why is a tree like a big dog?

They both have a lot of bark!

What do you call a dog magician?

A labracadabrador

What do you call a frozen dog?

A pupsicle

What do you get when you cross a dog and a calculator?

A friend you can count on

What do you get when you cross a dog with a frog?

A dog that can lick you from across the road.

Why did the dog cross the road?

To get to the "barking" lot

How are a dog and a marine biologist alike?

One wags a tail and the other tags a whale

What does a dog scientist do with the bones?

Barium

What do you get if you cross a cocker spaniel, a poodle, and a rooster?

A cockerpoodledoo

What is a dog's favorite food?

Anything that is on your plate

Why do dogs wag their tails?

Because no one will do it for them

Why are dogs like phones?

Because they have collar IDs

# On the Road Again

What's the best thing about car travel? Well, that's a no-brainer. You might see adorable dogs on the way. With just a little planning, you can turn this cuteness quest into a fun and FUR-bulous game!

Just follow these simple rules.

## HOW TO PLAY

Before the journey begins, each player guesses how many dogs he or she will see during the trip. If you think you're going to see three pups on the way to the grocery store, for instance, your magic number is three.

Every player must choose a different number. No duplications!

Take your route and distance into account to make a good guess.

## DOG TALLY

- Grocery store
- School
- Park
- Doctor's office
- After-school activity
- Best friend's house
- Vacation
- Mall
- Sports or band practice
- Dance or gymnastics
- Other

Keep a running total of the dogs you see on the way to various places. Check a box for every dog you see.

The game starts when the car starts moving. Look for dogs on the sidewalks, in front yards, in other peoples' cars, in parks, and anywhere else you can see along the way. Keep a running count of the dogs that every player sees.

When you reach your destination, whoever gets closest to his or her total number without going over wins.

# Glamour Pup Gallery

The oldest dog recorded was twenty-six years old and lived in Japan.

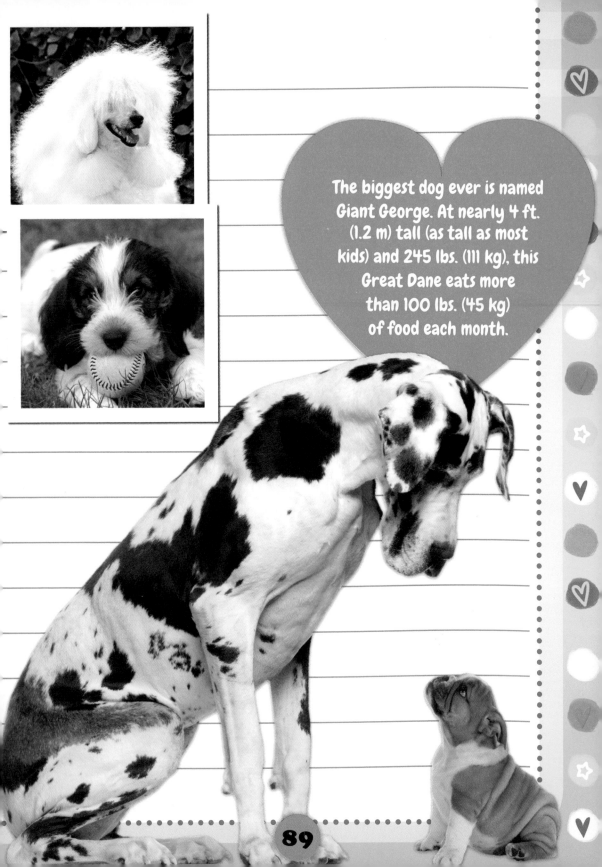

The biggest dog ever is named Giant George. At nearly 4 ft. (1.2 m) tall (as tall as most kids) and 245 lbs. (111 kg), this Great Dane eats more than 100 lbs. (45 kg) of food each month.

The most puppies in a litter came from a mommy dog that had twenty-four puppies. Bowwow! That's a lot of brothers and sisters!

A dog was the world's first animal Earth orbiter. The Soviet Union launched Laika into space in the 1957 Sputnik flight.

# Answers

## How did you do?

From pages 12–13

From page 55

| | | | | | | | ¹C | O | A | T |
| | | | | ²F | | | H | | | |
| | | ³C | O | L | L | I | E | | | |
| | | A | | E | | | H | | | |
| | | N | | A | | | U | | | |
| | | I | | S | | | A | | | |
| | ⁴B | N | | | | | H | | |
| ⁵T | O | N | G | U | E | | A | ⁶P | U | P | ⁷P | Y |
| | N | | | | | | | | | A |
| ⁸V | E | T | | | | | | | | C |
| | | | | | | | | ⁹B | A | R | K |
| | | | | | | | | A | | |
| | | | | | | | | L | | |
| | | | | | | ¹⁰L | E | A | S | H |

From pages 18–19

From pages 28–29

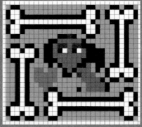

## From page 71

**My favorite game to play is fetch.**

**You are my best friend.**

**Bones are my favorite treats.**

Let's go play outside.

**Please take me for a walk.**

Watch me do a trick.

## From pages 64–65

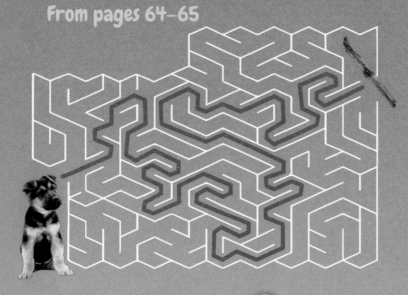

From pages 72–73

**TRAINING**

BONE

**WATCHDOG**

TRICKS

**PLAYTIME**

BARK

**CRATE**

LEASH

**FURRY**

WHINE

**TERRIER**

PLAYFUL

**LITTER**

LABRADOR

**COLLIE**

BEAGLE

**BOXER**

HUSKY

From page 78

N N A M R E B O D D T U K J G
M A S T I F F S C N S Z M Q O
N T I E P R A H S A W T O Q D
Z O H T T E O P M L D H H C L
R G L R A W I O I D J I B O L
E O I L C M Y L B N H C X E U
W T T H I E L E L U S H N R B
E R O T D P A A A C H N E R D
I W E D W G A H D F E A R N T
D P T L E U P A W S E U W E
A N O E R A I T I E T O Z S R
R U I P A I I L G N H J E V R
A O N P O K E N E D U T R I I
N H T I A Q I V O R L R P K E
E Y E H H K Y O E A L U Q U R
R E R W E O L B M R G L W L O
G R R P E B D N U H S H C A D
S G S P O M E R A N I A N S Q

From pages 80–81

#smile

I ♥ PUPS

#BFF

Printed in Jiaxing, China    528307   10/16